15 party pieces for piano

Alan Bullard

CONTENTS

The Associated Board of the Royal Schools of Music

to Janet and her pupils

Holiday Fanfare

ALAN BULLARD

Note: metronome marks in all pieces are given as a guide only.

AB 2698

Tennis Match

On the Beach

Woodland Walk

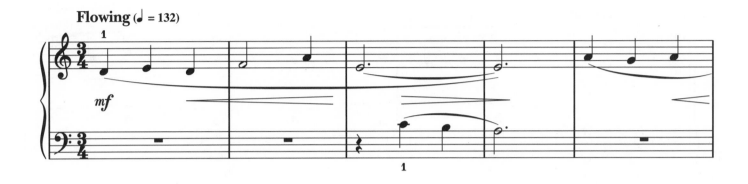

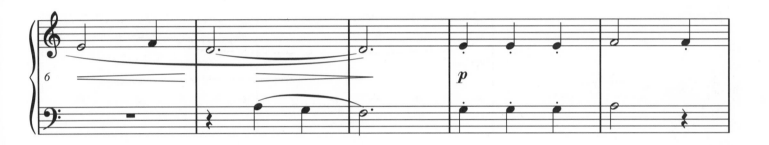

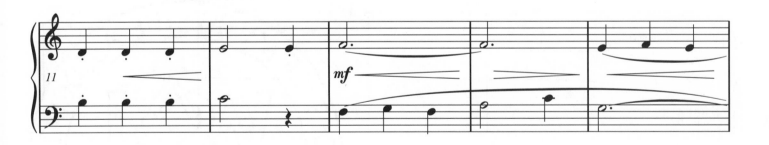

Relaxing by the Pool

Hold down the sustaining pedal throughout.

Seaside Rock

On the Swings

Rainy Day

Use the sustaining pedal as marked, to blur the sound in the first and last sections,
and keep the soft pedal down throughout.

End of the Pier

Beneath the Sea

Picnic Lunch

Mountain Climbing

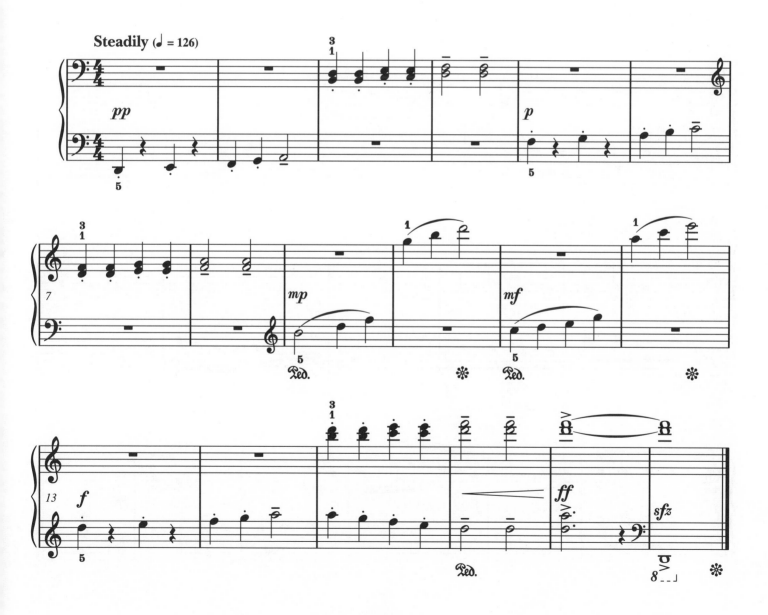

Fairground

Dodgems

Ice-Skating

Throughout this piece the right hand is on the black notes
and the left hand on the white notes.

Printed by Caligraving Limited Thetford Norfolk England   AB 2698   4:98